STORYBOOK

Created by Barry Smith

Stories by
Brenda Apsley, Clive Hopwood,
Glynis Langley and Hilda Young

CLIVEDEN PRESS

contents

Published in Great Britain by Cliveden Press,
An Egmont Company, Egmont House, P.O. Box 111,
Great Ducie Street, Manchester M60 3BL.
Printed in Singapore. ISBN 0 7235 2490 4

TREASURE HUNT

After a long hard winter, spring had come at last to Countrylane. Catkins hung like lambs' tails on the hazel trees; the yellow coltsfoot was in flower in the ditches; primroses and white violets peeped shyly among the grass in the woods, and all the birds were busy searching for twigs, moss and feathers to build their nests.

Everyone in Countrylane was busy spring cleaning, even Ramsbottom and Hubert, helped by Granny Hermione and Mrs Badger.

"Oh, Sammy, do go away and play," pleaded Mrs Squirrel, brushing her son out of the house with her birch broom.

COUNTRY CODE

Never take an egg from a bird's nest, and never disturb the nest in any way. Never pick wild flowers: leave them alone for others to enjoy.

So Sammy went off down the lane in search of his friends. He found Cedric and Charlotte, and the Rabbit twins, Rona and Reggie, gathered around the old oak. As he drew nearer Sammy saw that there was a notice pinned to the tree. It said:

COUNTRYLANE TREASURE HUNT

If the treasure you wish to seek,
Find the kettle with a leak.

An oak tree grows from a tiny acorn. Lots of wild animals such as squirrels eat acorns for food. Long ago ships were made from oak wood because it was strong and durable. Oak leaves are pale green in spring, rich green in summer and in the autumn they turn to golden-brown.

"We haven't solved the clue yet," said Cedric. "Do you know who has a leaky kettle, Sammy?"

But before Sammy could answer, the cuckoo, who was flying around Countrylane telling everyone spring had arrived, called out: "Look under the hedge near Granny Hermione's house."

Before they could ask him why, the cuckoo had flown on. So, since no one else had any ideas, they set off towards Granny Hamster's house.

Countryfolk call the cuckoo 'the herald of spring'. The lazy cuckoo lays her eggs in another bird's nest. When the baby cuckoo hatches out he is so greedy and big that he finally pushes all the other baby birds out of the nest so that he can have the nest to himself!

And just under the hedgerow near Granny Hermione's house was a kettle . . .the new home of Robbie Robin. "Granny gave it to me when it started to leak," he explained to the astonished children. "See how comfortable I have made it for us. I suppose you have come for your next clue. Listen!" And the robin sang:

Near the stream where the willow weeps,
An old tadpole your next clue keeps.

"If you put your thinking caps on, you should soon solve this one," chuckled the robin as he flew off to Hermione's for some scraps to feed his new family.

THE ROBIN

Robins build their nests everywhere . . . in a tree or bank, in an old kettle, in a church and even indoors in a cupboard. Both Cock Robin and his wife have a red breast. They eat fruit, berries, and insects. Robin eggs are white, speckled with red.

"Tadpoles live in streams," said Rona quickly. "Shall we go there next?"

The others nodded in agreement.

Then suddenly Cedric said: "I think this is a jokey clue. It said an old tadpole. Well, an old tadpole . . ."

"Ernest Frog!" everyone cried together. "Ernest is an old tadpole! Tadpoles do change to frogs."

Off they set once again, running swiftly over the bridge to where Ernest was fishing.

"I see you've managed to find this old tadpole," chuckled Ernest, as they flopped down beside him near a carpet of white wood anemones.
"Well, it was Cedric who thought that you might be the old tadpole," cried Bill Beaver, who had only just caught up with the others.
"Cedric, was it?" murmured Ernest, giving the little shrew a smile. "Well, you may be small, my lad, but you're certainly shrewd."

Everyone laughed at the frog's little joke, and Cedric and Charlotte looked very pleased. Sometimes people made jokes about their size, and it did annoy them!

"Have you got the next clue for us, Ernest?" asked Rona eagerly. "Well, take a look in my fishing basket and see," suggested Ernest with a twinkle in his eye.
Rona peered into the basket and then she pulled out a small piece of paper. On it was written:

If the next clue you wish to know
To the oldest inhabitant you must go!

SHREWS

When these tiny little creatures are angry, they shoot out a nasty-smelling liquid all over their enemy! They can eat twice their own weight each day, and they are the smallest of all the woodland mammals. They have long, pointed noses, small ears and very short teeth.

15

"Oh dear, the oldest inhabitant!" gasped Sammy Squirrel. "That is a hard one!"

"Why?" asked Bill Beaver, who had only recently come to live in Countrylane. "Surely that is either Great Uncle Hubert or Granny Hermione?"

COUNTRY CODE

Always close gates behind you, and keep to the footpath. Do not climb over walls, use the stiles, and **never** push your way through a hedge.

16

"Because they will never tell us how old they are," explained Sammy. "We know they went to school together but ..."

"Well, we shall just have to go and see them both," suggested Rona Rabbit sensibly. "Let's try Great Uncle Hubert first."

"Good luck, I hope you find your next clue," cried Ernest, as he peered into the stream to see if there were any fish about.

But when they got to Great Uncle Hubert's house it was empty.

"If he is the oldest inhabitant, we shall never get the clue!" cried Billl Beaver in disappointment. "He could be anywhere in Countrylane."

"Perhaps he has gone to see Granny Hermione," cried Reggie. "Come on, it's worth a try."

So the children set off once again, along the lane and through the fields to Hermione Hamster's house.

But when they knocked at the door she wasn't in either! "The treasure trail's lost!" cried Charlotte. "We've come to a dead end."

The little band started to trail off down the path, when suddenly Rona gave a little cry.

"There's something sticking out of Granny Hermione's water barrel!" she cried.

"It looks like a picture!" cried Bill Beaver, rushing over. He picked it up and showed it to the others. It was a picture of Hermione *and* Hubert and it said:

Your next clue we have carefully set,
You've all done well, but there's no treasure yet.

Hamsters are related to mice and they like nuts, grain and fruit to eat. Like all hamsters, Hubert and Hermione can store up food in their cheeks until they are hungry again. It's just like having a little larder in their mouths! Isn't that a clever trick?

"So we still don't know which of them is the oldest!" laughed Sammy. "But at least we've found the next clue."

19

Squirrels live in woods in the countryside. Red squirrels are rare, but grey squirrels are quite common, and may even be found in gardens. Squirrels go to sleep for short periods in the winter, but they often wake up, and nibble some of the nuts which they stored in the autumn.

"It's nice to know those wise old hamsters think we are doing well," said Reggie Rabbit. "But where is the clue they have set? Is that in the water barrel too?"

"No, there's nothing else here," replied Bill Beaver, peering inside the barrel again. "The clue must be in the rhyme. But what can it mean?"

Everyone thought very hard, and kept repeating the clue to themselves.

Then, suddenly Sammy started to laugh.
"Where do you live, Bill?" he asked.
"In Beaver Lodge, of course, you know that!" replied Bill.
"And where do I live?" chuckled Sammy. "In a *drey*, like all squirrels, and who lives in a *set*?"
"Professor Torquillian Badger!" cried Charlotte, clapping her paws in delight. "Oh, Sammy, what a clever squirrel you are!"

21

A badger gets his name from the **badge**, or black and white stripes on his face. A shy creature, he searches for food at night. He lines his set with bracken and grass and keeps it very clean . . . just like Torquillian!

Off everyone went to the Professor's house, eager to find the next clue.

They found Mrs Badger in the garden pegging out her washing . . .and Martin Mouse.

"He fell in my washing tub, so I'm hanging him out to dry," explained Mrs Badger. "You'll find the Professor in his laboratory, working on his experiments as usual. Go right in, he's expecting you."

"Aha, the treasure hunters, I see," cried Torquillian Badger, as the children entered after knocking politely at the door. "Just in time to see my latest invention. It's an umbrella you wear on your head. Do you like it?"
Everyone thought that Torquillian looked rather funny with an umbrella on his head, but they were too polite to say so.
Sammy coughed, and then said, "It will be very useful when it rains, sir."

"Just what I thought," cried Torquillian gleefully. "I'm making one for Hermione and Hubert, and one for Harold Hedgehog. His car has no hood, so it will keep him dry."

Hedgehogs hibernate during the winter months, and sleep the cold days away until spring comes again. They like insects and eggs to eat, and if you leave a saucer of milk out for them at night they will be very grateful to you.

"I suppose you are all waiting to hear my clue?" said Torquillian. "I've put it down somewhere!"

The children groaned. The Professor was always losing his papers . . .there were so many of them.

"We shall be here for hours," whispered Reggie to his twin.

But suddenly, Torquillian opened up a cupboard full of jars and bottles . . .and took out a bottle with a message in it.

"I was going to throw it into the stream for you," he explained.

"Please may we have it now that we are here?" asked Reggie politely. If the Professor got talking about sailors and ships in bottles, they would never get away.

Torquillian handed over the bottle, and he was back again with his experimenting before the Countrylane children were out of the door.

"What does it say?" Sammy cried, as Reggie struggled to get the message out of the bottle.

A male rabbit is called a **buck** and a female rabbit is a **doe**. Rabbits can run very fast when they are attacked, and they warm their families of any danger by thumping on the ground with their back feet, and showing their white bobtails.

But when Reggie read out the clue, everyone groaned in dismay. For this clue said:

Now here is your very last clue –
I'd start again if I were you.

"Oh, no, we can't do it all over again! Someone's been playing a cruel joke on us!" cried little Charlotte, beginning to cry.

"It does seem strange," admitted Sammy. "But folk are kind in Countrylane. There must be a reason for starting again. Come on, everyone, let's go back and read the notice again."

So, sadly, and very, very, slowly, for they were all very tired, they made their way back to the old oak tree.

And they were so downcast that they did not see Hubert and Hermione, Rufus and Cyril, Sarah and Marmaduke, and Edgar, Selina and old Ernest peeping at them through the trees.

But when they got to the oak tree, they saw, to their great surprise, that the notice had been changed. Now it read:
Well done, children, now climb the tree,
And the treasure there you'll see.

"The treasure's hidden in the branches of the tree! Hurray, we've found it at last!" cried the children.

"I'll climb the tree for the treasure!" cried Sammy. And away up the tree he went.

"There's a parcel of treasure for everyone here," he called as he peered into the leafy branches. "Catch the treasure as I throw it down!"

One by one Sammy threw down several small parcels, each one bearing the name of one of the treasure seekers.

Then Sammy leapt down and everyone opened their treasure.

Squirrels are very agile at climbing trees. They use their tails for extra balance, like a counterweight. Some naughty squirrels hide in a tree's leafy branches and pelt passers-by with nuts and acorns!

There was a pretty peg doll for Rona and Charlotte.
Sammy and Bill got a fine cricket bat each, and Cedric
got a little walnut shrew just like himself! And all the
children got a packet of honey sweets!
"Ben Beaver and Granny Hermione must have made the
treasure!" squeaked Charlotte in delight.
"Quite right, my dear," cried Hermione, stepping from
her hiding place. "Have you enjoyed your treasure
hunt?"
"It was lovely!" everyone cried. "Let's have another one
tomorrow!"

HAROLD HEDGEHOG TO THE RESCUE

Harold Hedgehog came out of his house and yawned. The April sun was bright, but there was still a distinct chill in the air, so Harold buttoned his coat up tight to keep warm. Harold's cottage was a pleasant little house, nestling on the edge of the woods overlooking the village.

Hedgehogs, like lots of animals, go to sleep for several months every year during the winter. This is called *hibernation*, and they feed themselves up in the autumn and make their houses warm and dry so that they can sleep comfortably through the cold months. You can often see them right up to Christmas, and they will become regular visitors to your doorstep if you leave a saucer of milk out for them.

All around him he could see the first signs of spring, as the hedgerows and woodlands burst into life. Anemone and celandine, bluebells, all showing their petals to the sun. Across the fields he could see pretty carpets of daisies, and further down the valley, along the riverbank, clouds of yellow daffodils flanked the fast flowing, babbling waters.

Hibernation

Hedgehogs hibernate from as early as October, until April. They make their nests dry and warm by covering them with pieces of moss and leaves. Frogs hibernate under water in a hole at the bottom of a ditch or pond, going to sleep during October and waking up in February.

Harold took a long look around his garden to see that everything was as it should be. The mistletoe looked healthy enough, its tiny flowers promising a bumper crop of berries for the birds next winter. Harold had always thought it such a lovely sight to see the birds come flocking down to the old oak tree in the garden, and he always tried to stay up as long as he dared in autumn to see his welcome friends come to feed from his mistletoe.

Mistletoe and Magic

The mistletoe has long been thought of as a magical plant. The Druids believed that an oak tree was sacred if mistletoe grew on it. The plant is often used at Christmas, as a symbol of peace. The berries though, are poisonous to human beings.

The hedgehog lives in a nest made of grass or leaves in open woods, fields, hedgerows and gardens. He comes out at night to look for food, which he finds with his keen senses of smell and hearing.

Down in the village he could see lots of his animal chums going about their daily chores. "My word, everybody *is* busy!" he thought to himself, which reminded him that as his little winter sleep was over, he too must get down to business.

His car was where he had left it, and he checked to see if it was topped up with berry juice for his ride down to the village. Harold always kept a large bush of bilberries next to where his car stood. The greeny-pink flowers, shaped rather like bells, were already beginning to blossom and Harold knew that if he was patient and waited a month or two they would produce luscious round berries, black and plump. He also knew that he loved bilberry jam, and had to be very strict with himself and not eat them all up, because without bilberries his motor car just would not go.

Harold was very proud of his motor car, and all the youngsters in the village thought it was a most marvellous machine. The older residents, like Granny Hermione Hamster and Great Uncle Hubert Hamster, weren't so sure it was a good thing, but Harold was convinced that, as editor of the *Countrylane News*, he must keep up with the times and set a modern example. He had just turned the corner into the lane when a great shout made him pull up sharply.

A Nature Notebook

Keep a nature notebook of all the birds, animals and plants you see on a country walk. Make drawings beside your notes and pick up fallen leaves to stick in your book. Don't pick the flowers though. Leave them for other people to enjoy.

"I say, look out, will you!" said Ernest Frog crossly, jumping out of a ditch. "Oh, I might have known it was you and that infernal contraption."

"It's a motor car," replied Harold calmly, "and I haven't run you over so don't tell lies. I honked my horn as I came round the corner."

Frogs

Frogs are *amphibians*, which means they can live both on land and in water. Their skin is soft, smooth and moist and can change colour.

"I know," said Ernest, dusting off his coat and rearranging his scarf. "It was your horn that made me fall into the ditch...but not for much longer, oh, no, you'll see."

Harold was most confused by this, but before he could speak, Ernest was off down the road. Harold decided Ernest was in one of his more grumpy moods, and before long he had forgotten it altogether, as he steered his car along the narrow, twisting lane. "Ah, the open road," he murmured happily, and was soon in the village where he

stopped outside the shop.
Rufus Rabbit was just coming out, carrying several packets of seeds to plant in his fields. Harold greeted him with a big smile. "Good morning, Rufus! Spring is here at last then."
Rufus merely nodded briefly and bounded away.

What Rabbits Eat

Rabbits often eat more than a pound of fresh green food a day. Food is eaten and then excreted in semi-digested pellets to be eaten again and fully digested. Lots of dry pellets can often be seen lying on the ground where rabbits have been.

"Dearie me," said Harold. "Here I am, only woken up from my winter sleep this morning, haven't seen anybody since before Christmas, and not a friendly face in sight. What *is* the matter with everyone?"

Isabel Mouse's shop was a treasure trove of all sorts of interesting things — pots and pans of all shapes and sizes, brooms and buckets, pots of paint, all manner of food, big books, small books, bicycle pumps, dishcloths and candles . .in fact, it was often difficult to find Isabel at all, among all her goods.

42

The bell on the door jangled as Harold entered. "Ah, hello Isabel. A lovely spring day, isn't it?" said Harold, looking round the shop. "I'd like a sharp, new pencil and a writing pad, please. I have to write this year's first edition of *Countrylane News*, and I'd like to get started straight away."

"Oh, it's you, Harold," said Isabel, nervously.
"Well, of course it's me. Really! Anybody would think you all wanted me to go back to sleep, and *stay* asleep all the year round." Harold was beginning to feel a little bit unwanted, for although he had been friendly to everyone he had met, nobody seemed in the least bit pleased to see him.

43

"A pencil and a pad, you said," went on Isabel quickly, anxious to change the subject.

Harold looked at her, puzzled. Most of the stories he put in his newspaper came from Isabel, because she met so many people in her shop every day, and picked up lots of fascinating pieces of news. Harold was slowly becoming suspicious that an important item of news was being kept secret from him, and he told Isabel so.

"Oh, but I couldn't possibly tell, I really couldn't," said Isabel, getting upset. "But I want you to know I don't agree with it, and I'm on your side." With that, she gave Harold his pencil and paper, and rushed into the back of the shop.

A Mouse's Tail

A mouse's tail is very important, because it uses it to support itself as if it were an extra limb. The tail is very strong and can coil round anything.

Harold didn't know what to make of this at all, and putting the money for the things on the counter, he went out to his car. "That's the last straw!" he cried, getting in and slamming the door. "I'm going to get to the bottom of this right now. I shall go and see Great Uncle Hubert Hamster — he's bound to know what's happening."

He'd hardly gone a hundred yards, however, when a large notice, which was hanging on an oak tree, caught his attention. It was an enormous sheet of paper that almost stretched right round the great old tree and it was full from top to bottom with writing.

At the top were the words GRAND PUBLIC MEETING, and then an extremely long sentence all about keeping the countryside clean and beautiful. "Quite right, too," he commented.

At the bottom, in the corner, it said *Please turn over,* and with great difficulty, Harold crawled in between the notice and the tree to read the other side.

A minute later he burst through the middle of it, his eyes wide with horror.

"A grand public meeting to decide that motor cars will definitely be banned from using the lane?!" he spluttered. "They can't do this, I won't allow it! I shall jolly well go to their meeting and tell them so!"

Spring

Spring is the time when the countryside wakes up from its long winter sleep. Plants and trees begin to put out new shoots and buds, and many new-born animals appear. It is a time when all life is renewed.

The soft, gentle light of dusk had descended like a misty blanket over the fields. As Harold drove his trusty motor car down through the lanes he waved at little Rona Rabbit, out for her usual evening walk. At least someone was pleased to see him, he thought, and he pulled up at the side of the road to have a few words with his young friend.

"Hello, young Rona," he beamed happily. "Such a beautiful evening, isn't it?"

"Oh yes it is," laughed Rona, bounding over to his side. "I'm awfully sorry about everyone trying to get rid of your motor car. I really am."

"Don't you worry," replied Harold. "They've not beaten me yet, not by a long chalk. You'll see."

"Oh, I do hope so," said Rona. "But you won't tell anyone I said so, will you?"

"Why no, of course not," answered Harold. "Your father seemed very nervous about it all when I met him this morning, so I promise not to say a word. Where is he by the way?"

Rona pointed across the fields.

Oaks are tall, wide trees which grow from little acorns. Some oaks grow as high as 12 metres and are hundreds of years old. There are many oak trees in Britain, and their wood is very good for making boats and furniture and for building houses that will last for a very long time.

"He and my brother Reggie have gone to look for something special for supper in the woods," she explained, "but he said he'd be back in time for the meeting. I hope you win."

"Well, thank you, young Rona," smiled Harold. "And if I do, I promise to take you for a long ride in my motor car. Would you like that?"

"Oh yes, please," squealed Rona in delight, "but only if my Daddy says so."

"Quite right, very wise," agreed Harold. "Now I must be off, or I shall be late. Take care. Toodle-oo!"

49

With that, he drove off and continued his journey down to the village. A large crowd had assembled on the village green for the meeting. Ernest Frog, together with Great Uncle Hubert Hamster, was trying to quieten everyone down so that they could begin, but the crowd fell suddenly silent as Reggie, one of Rufus Rabbit's youngsters, came bounding up, out of breath and with a look of terror on his face.

Baby rabbits are born underground. At first they cannot see or hear, and have no fur. Within a month they can look after themselves, and reach adult size in nine months.

"Oh, come quickly, come quickly," he panted. "Father is caught in a trap and I think he will die if we don't release him straight away." Once the little rabbit had calmed down, they managed to find out where his father was. "And you've run all this way?" asked Great Uncle Hubert. "Why, that must be all of three miles. We'll never get there in time."

"Oh yes, we will," said a voice behind them. "We can go in my car, and we'll be there in no time."
No sooner had Harold said it, than Ben Beaver, Granny Hermione Hamster and Reggie were all packed into the little car and Harold was speeding to the rescue.

Harold's little car flew like the wind through the village, rattling loose stones and scattering startled latecomers on their way to the meeting. The road wound ahead through the darkness like a ribbon, twisting and turning through the hills and the woods as the car sped on its errand of mercy.

"Oh, my goodness," cried Granny Hermione Hamster, clutching on to her hat, which threatened to fly off at any moment.

"Can't it go any faster?" urged little Reggie, peering out through the windscreen at the dark road in front of them.

"Hang on," said Harold, driving as fast and as carefully as he could. "We don't want to knock anybody down on the way. What's the good of saving one life if you take another? We'll get there in time, don't you worry, young Reggie."

In days long gone by, when the Navy used to build ships out of wood, it took as much as 2,000 tonnes of oak to build a ship.

54

And Harold was as good as his word. Hurtling along at almost twenty miles an hour, Harold's little car covered the distance from the village to the spot where Rufus lay injured in less than ten minutes!

Woods and Forests

There are many beautiful woods and forests in our countryside where you will find many varieties of plants and animals that live there. Next time you go out to the country try and collect all the different kind's of fallen leaves you can find. Ask your Mummy or Daddy to help you find their pictures in a book so that you can learn their names.

In next to no time, Ben Beaver had gnawed open the trap with his strong teeth, and Granny Hermione Hamster had applied some of her soothing herbs and bandaged up the rabbit's damaged paw. They were home within the hour, and Rufus was soon tucked up safely in bed.

"Well," said Ernest Frog, as they all gathered round Great Uncle Hubert's fireplace later that evening, "I'll have to admit I was wrong. Motor cars do have their uses sometimes."

"And you've got your headline for the first copy of this year's *Countrylane News*," added Granny Hermione Hamster. **"Harold Hedgehog's Motor Car Saves Rufus Rabbit."**

Harold smiled contentedly, and all his friends raised three cheers for the village's new hero.

THE
MYSTERY

Granny Hermione Hamster was very excited. She had
seen the postman coming up the garden path – and he
was carrying a small parcel. As he lifted the knocker on
the door it opened wide. "Morning, Hermione," he said.
"Looks like you were expecting this, eh?"
"Yes, yes, indeed I was," said Hermione, taking the small
parcel. "Thank you, thank you *very* much." She waved as
the postman walked on up the lane, then hurried indoors.

Hermione laid the parcel on the table, then quickly ripped open the brown paper. There lay a tiny new garden trowel, no bigger than her paw. "Just perfect for my herb garden," she said, turning the shiny trowel and letting it glint in the early morning sunlight that streamed through the window of the cottage. "I'll try it out as soon as the dew has disappeared!"

The Golden Hamster is a popular pet. The Golden Hamster was not really known until 1930, when an adult female and twelve young were found in Syria. Some of the offspring were sent to England in 1931, and the Golden Hamster was soon established as a favourite pet.

Hermione sat in her rocking chair with a cup of tea, and from time to time her eyes moved to the tiny new trowel. She could hardly wait to try it out.

As soon as the dew had disappeared, Hermione went out into the garden and knelt at the herb bed. She picked some peppermint leaves – perfect for my elevenses, she thought – and some marigolds to make into marigold water. She had promised some to Isabel to ease her aching feet. Then she started to weed among the neat rows of herbs with the shiny new trowel; it was just right!

Hermione knew all about herbal remedies; that marigolds help ease aching feet, for instance. The flowers should be picked when the dew has disappeared, then washed and bruised in a pestle and mortar. Boiling water should be poured over them; then, when it has cooled, the flowers should be strained off. The remaining marigold water should be cooled, and used as a foot bath. Always ask an adult to help if you are using boiling water.

THYME

CHI E

EY

NT

Going back into the kitchen, Hermione made up the marigold water for Isabel.

While the marigold water cooled, Hermione made herself a refreshing mug of peppermint tea, and sat in her rocking chair to enjoy it.

Did you think it unusual that Hermione drank peppermint tea rather than ordinary tea? Hamsters eat and drink all sorts of things which we do not. As a matter of fact many things which animals eat and drink can actually be poisonous to humans.

As she sipped at her peppermint tea, Hermione glanced out of the window. Dark clouds were rolling over the hills. "It looks like rain," she said. "I'd better go and bring in my new trowel — I don't want it to go rusty."

There are lots of country saying that foretell the weather. Why not look out for these signs, and see if they really do foretell the weather?

If swallows fly low,
the weather will be bad.
If spiders desert their webs
for sheltered places,
rain is sure to fall.
Red sky at night,
shepherd's delight;
red sky at morning,
shepherd's warning.

Hermione rushed out to her herb garden, but the trowel was nowhere to be seen. "Well!" said Hermione, straightening up and putting her hands on her hips. "I *know* it was here a few minutes ago!"

Just then Harold Hedgehog came along the lane in his shiny old car. He stopped outside the gate and raised his hat. "Morning," he said. "How are you today?"

"Well, Harold," Hermione answered. "I'm very puzzled." Her eyes still searched among the narrow gaps between the rows of herbs. "I had my new trowel out here just a few minutes ago, and now it's disappeared." She pushed aside a large clump of mint. "It *must* be here somewhere . . ."

"Funny you should say that," said Harold, "because I lost something rather mysteriously myself, only yesterday. I bought a new chrome motor horn — fitted it myself — and what do you know if it hadn't disappeared a couple of hours later!"

"Mmmm," said Hermione, not really listening. "Now where *is* that trowel . . ."

Hedgehogs are often known as a gardener's best friend. Why? Because they eat lots of garden pests, yet do no harm to his flowers and vegetables.

"Tell you what," Harold suggested, "I'm going to put a notice in this week's *Countrylane News* about my horn. Would you like me to mention your trowel?"
Hermione straightened up again and smoothed down her apron. "I think you'd better, Harold," she said. "I know it seems silly, but that trowel has just disappeared."

A notice appeared on the front page the next day:

VALUABLE ITEMS DISAPPEAR

Anyone knowing the whereabouts of one chrome motor horn and one small trowel should notify the editor immediately. All information will be treated in the strictest confidence.

But no one came forward with any information. The only person to call at the newspaper office was Cyril Squirrel. He hadn't found the horn and the trowel; he had a loss of his own to report. "It's my spectacles," he told Harold. "They're lost, and *I'm* lost without them. Now I *know* that I am rather forgetful, but I distinctly remember leaving them under the hazel tree. I never wear them when I'm gathering nuts, in case they slip off my nose and smash to the ground. When I came to put my spectacles on again, they'd disappeared!"

"Curiouser and curiouser, I must say," said Harold Hedgehog. "Come on, I think we should go and seek Torquillian Badger's advice. He'll know what to do. We'll pick up Hermione on the way."

The three friends drove up to Torquillian Badger's set and knocked at the door, which was opened by Mrs Badger. Hot swirling clouds of steam escaped from the kitchen, and Mrs Badger held three wooden clothespegs clamped firmly between her teeth. "Er, I do hope that we haven't called at an inconvenient moment," said Harold. "May we talk to the Professor?"

Mrs Badger took the clothespegs from her mouth and pointed to the bottom of the garden. "He's down there in the shed," she said. "Experimenting, or whatever he calls it. Please, go on down. I must get back to my washing."

Badgers live in a system of underground burrows called a set. Badgers have coarse, dark-coloured fur with a white blaze on the forehead. They hibernate through the winter months, and guard their homes and territories very fiercely. The badger is sometimes known as **brock.**

As the three friends approached the shed they heard strange noises from within. Harold knocked and waited, but nothing happened. He knocked again then with a 'well, he's like that' shrug, he walked in.

Harold peered through a haze of thick grey smoke that filled the small shed. "Professor Badger?" he asked, rubbing his eyes.

A dark shape loomed towards him. "Hello, friends!" boomed the loud voice of Professor Torquillian Badger. "I've just been experimenting to find a use for empty conker shells; there are an awful lot of them around, you know."

The Professor coughed. "Conclusion number one has now been reached: empty conker shells do *not* make a good fuel source." He took a bucket of water and threw it over the still-smouldering conker shells, then mopped his brow with a large spotted handkerchief as an even thicker cloud of black smoke filled the shed. "Come on, let's talk outside."

Safely outside in the fresh air, the Professor listened carefully as the three friends explained their problem. "Our things have just disappeared," said Harold when they had told their stories. "It's a complete mystery."
The Professor scratched at his left ear thoughtfully. "Mmmm," he mused. "You certainly have a very interesting problem. Let me think about it, will you? Tell you what, call back later this afternoon; I'll have had time to read up on this by then." And with a cheery wave Torquillian Badger disappeared back into his shed.

Do you play conkers? Horse-chestnuts are hardened, then threaded onto string. One player hits his conker against his opponent's; the winner is the one that **doesn't** crack.

At the agreed time that afternoon, Harold took Hermione and Cyril back to the set, and this time they decided not to bother Mrs Badger, who had her hands full, pegging out dozens of socks on a long washing line that stretched from the side of the door right down to the bottom of the orchard. The three friends went straight to the garden shed.

They found Professor Badger poring over a huge old leather-bound book. He motioned with his paw, not taking his eyes from the page that he was reading. "Sit down, sit down," he said. "I'll be with you in just a moment."

After looking around the cramped shed at the chairs, which were all piled high with precarious stacks of books, papers, microscopes, scientific papers (and a few chocolate biscuits) Harold gave another of his 'well, he's like that' shrugs, and leant against a bookcase.

After what seemed like an hour – but was in fact just a few minutes – Professor Badger looked up. "Mmmm, good," he said. "Now, to solve the mystery, I must ask you some questions about these disappearances."

The Professor turned to Harold. "Firstly, am I right in thinking that all the objects which disappeared are shiny?" Harold thought for a moment. "Yes," he said. "And that they were all lost out in the open?" "That's right," said Harold. "And am I right in thinking that a pair of magpies have recently moved into that big elm tree in the meadow?" Harry couldn't see the significance of that question, but nodded anyway: "That's right."

Professor Badger jumped to his feet and flung open the shed door. "Come on!" he called over his shoulder. "To the meadow!"

Have you ever seen a magpie? They are easily identified birds, especially in flight, with their short wings and long, tapering tail. They are about 45cm long, and have bold black and white plumage. They eat insects and grain, and have become unpopular with gamekeepers as they will rob other birds' nests of eggs and young, mainly partridge and pheasant.

Do you know the well-known rhyme about seeing magpies?

One for sorrow, two for joy;
   Three for a girl, four for a boy;
      Five for silver, six for gold;
         Seven for a secret never to be told.

The four piled into Harold's car, and after a short drive they arrived at the meadow. They strode through the tall grass, and were soon standing beneath the old elm tree, looking up into its lush green foliage. "Look, up there!" said the Professor, pointing high into the branches. "Do you see the magpies' nest up there?" The three friends nodded, and wondered what on earth the Professor was doing.

There are lots of superstitions connected with magpies. If a magpie should perch on your roof, there is no danger of the house falling down; if you see two magpies flying while you are fishing, your catch will be a good one. In some places it is the custom to spit three times when a magpie is seen, or ill luck will follow.

The Professor turned to Cyril. "You do see the nest, don't you?" he asked. Cyril couldn't see as clearly as he could with his spectacles on, but the magpies' nest was unmistakable, and he nodded. "Right," said the Professor, "climb up there, would you, and bring down whatever you find in the nest?"

The magpie was formerly known as the maggot-pie. *Maggot* represented the name Margaret, and *pie* was derived from pied, referring to the bird's distinctive black and white pied plumage.

Bishops were referred to derisively as magpies, because of their black and white vestments.

Cyril was just about to ask the Professor what on earth he wanted with magpie eggs when he was silenced by a paw placed on his lips. "No questions just yet, eh?" said Torquillian wisely. Then, with an air of mystery he added: "All will be revealed — later!"

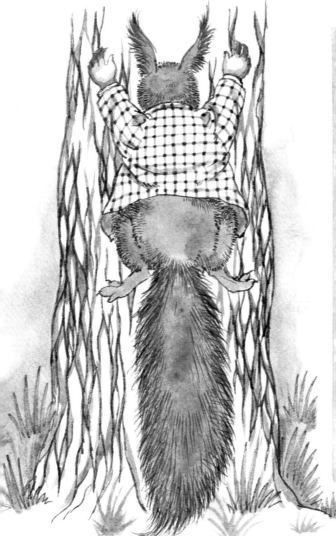

Look out for squirrels when you are out in the country, especially where there are lots of conifer trees. You may be lucky enough to see a red squirrel, but grey squirrels are more common. They are agile and graceful, climbing tree trunks with ease, and leaping from branch to branch. The squirrel's favourite foods include acorns, beech-nuts, pine seeds and toadstools, and these are often hoarded. The squirrel's nest (known as a drey) is made of interlaced twigs lined with moss. A deserted magpie's nest is sometimes used as a foundation for the drey.

Cyril scurried up the elm's thick old trunk in a trice, and disappeared into the nest until only the tip of his bushy tail could be seen.

When Cyril emerged from the nest he ran back down the elm tree's broad trunk and stopped in front of the Professor. He held something small and shiny in his paw – it was Hermione's tiny trowel! Harold and Hermione gasped in amazement and looked at each other. Harold was about to speak when a raised paw from the Professor silenced him.

"There's more!" said Cyril, and in a second he was once again scampering to the top of the elm tree.

Do you know what an elm tree looks like? This is the shape of the tree:

And this is what the elm leaves look like:

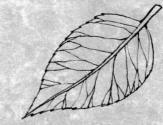

When he came down the elm tree for the second time Harold and Hermione watched him carefully. Yes — there he was, they could just see him through the green leaves. And he was carrying something else!

When Cyril was standing in front of them they saw just what he was carrying. It was Harold Hedgehog's shiny new motor horn! Cyril handed the horn to Harold and scampered off again up the elm tree.

"Well, I'll be blowed!" said Harold.

Magpies certainly have been known to pick up shiny objects in their beaks, and carry them back to their nests. They have quite a strong hoarding instinct, and will often store surplus food in the nest. Their cousins, jackdaws and jays, are well known for this behaviour too.

This time, when Cyril rushed down the tree trunk again, he wasn't carrying anything – but he *was* wearing his missing spectacles! "All three things were lying right inside that magpies' nest!" said Cyril excitedly. "How did you know just where to look, Professor?"

"Yes," said Hermione. "My trowel, what did they . . ."

"Yes," Harold Hedgehog interrupted. "How on earth did you know the magpies had our things, Torquillian?"

Professor Torquillian Badger silenced all three of his friends with a raised paw. "I'll tell you how I knew where the things were," he said. "When you had gone home this morning, I looked through an old book I have which deals with country lore and fables – my father left it to me, as a matter of fact. Anyway, I read that magpies are sometimes attracted to bright, shiny objects – no one knows why. Seems that they sometimes fly down, pick them up – and take them back to their nests. Since the magpies had moved in here recently, it seemed that they were the likely culprits."

Harold gave his motor horn a large squeeze. "And by jove you were right, Professor! Well done!"

"Yes, bravo!" Cyril added.

Just then, Hermione's keen eyes spotted two shapes flying high over the meadow towards them. It was the two magpies, and they were flying towards their home in the old elm. "What do you think the magpies will do when they find that their collection has disappeared?" she asked.

"Well, *I* solved the mysterious disappearances today," said Professor Badger, turning and striding away. "Let's leave the magpies with their own mystery to solve, eh? Come *on!*" he called over his shoulder, and the four friends hurried away to Harold's car.

BEN BEAVER'S BUSY DAY

It was a sunny morning in early summer down in Countrylane. A beautiful Red Admiral butterfly perched on a bright yellow dandelion and surveyed the peaceful scene.

The dandelion gets its name from the shape of its tooth-like leaves, *dent-de-lion,* which is French for lion's tooth. Rufus loves dandelion salad and Hermione makes wine from dandelion flowers.

In a nearby meadow Rufus Rabbit was busy working in his garden. As he weeded his carrot and lettuce patch, Rufus gave a sigh. He could hear his twins, Rona and Reggie, playing down by the stream with Cedric and Charlotte, the two little shrews. Just by the old dry stone wall Rufus caught sight of Ramsbottom Rat. Ramsbottom was lying in a hammock enjoying the sun.

"Well, I suppose he does need a rest after all his travels," murmured Rufus to himself. "I wish I could stop for a rest. Still, everyone enjoys my lettuces. So I suppose all my hard work is worthwhile."

There are lots of stone walls still standing in the northern counties of Britain. Dry stone walls are made by placing stones in certain positions so that they stand firm without any mortar. It is a very old and skilled country craft.

Meanwhile, down by the stream, Great Uncle Hubert Hamster sat on a bench reading a copy of *Countrylane News*. Despite the warmth of the sun, Hubert still wore his pale mauve and white muffler.

"My old bones still feel a chill," he would say, "even though I take a glass of Hermione's elderberry wine every morning."

Hubert was one of the oldest inhabitants of Countrylane. He had gone to school with Granny Hermione Hamster more years ago than either of them cared to remember ....but they were still the best of friends, and both were very highly regarded by everyone else in Countrylane, especially the children. Whenever anyone was in trouble

they always went to Hermione or Hubert for help and advice, knowing that these two hamsters were the wisest animals in Countrylane.

Perched on the edge of the bench, wearing his best polka-dot shirt was young Martin Mouse, one of the many folk who claimed kinship with Hubert. Martin had brought a packet of cheese sandwiches and a bag of seeds in case they felt hungry. He knew that Great Uncle Hubert's appetite had not waned with age, and that the old hamster just loved grain and seeds.

The children of Countrylane are always fascinated by the way Hubert can store up seeds in his cheeks until he needs them. It's just like having a larder inside his mouth!

Hamsters love to eat seeds and grain of every kind. The seeds of the dwarf mallow are a favourite meal of Hermione, but human beings cannot eat them. They are poisonous to humans.

Ernest Frog, who lived in a rather damp little house in the bulrushes was fishing contentedly on the bank of the stream. Hubert and Martin knew just how important it was to keep quiet when someone was fishing, so they were talking in whispers so that the fish would not know anyone was there.

But suddenly Edgar Stoat came along with a bucket to fill with water from the stream. As he put the bucket in the water it made a great splash and dozens of tiny minnows swam away in great fright.

"Now look what you've done!" grumbled Ernest. "There'll be no more fishing for me today. You really are a nuisance, Edgar!"

"I am so sorry, Ernest," cried Edgar, looking very upset. He knew many of the Countrylane folk were suspicious of stoats, and he really was a friendly fellow, despite his disturbing habit of changing the colour of his fur from brown to white in winter. "Mrs Badger needs the water to wash her kitchen floor. The pump has run dry. I was only trying to help. I didn't mean to scare the fish away!"

"Oh well, perhaps I was a little hasty," admitted Ernest. "The fish weren't biting at all today. I couldn't even catch a minnow!'

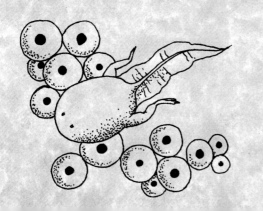

A tadpole turns into a frog, which is an amphibian. This means a frog can live both on land and in the water.

92

Minnows are tiny fish of the carp family. They are so small that they are not normally caught on a line.

Suddenly Ernest noticed Sarah and Marmaduke strolling towards him. Ernest smiled to himself. Sarah was wearing *another* new hat! It was white and it had a long silk scarf around the brim which matched the material of her dress. Sarah was always a very fashionable mouse! But, knowing the grass was still slippery with the morning dew, Ernest called out a warning.

"Take care, Sarah!" shouted Ernest. "The grass is very wet." But his warning came too late and, as she stumbled, the mischievous wind caught Sarah's hat and whirled it away towards the stream.

The stoat belongs to the weasel family, and nature has made the stoat a fierce hunter. His prey includes rabbits, squirrels and shrews.

"Oh, my lovely hat!" cried Sarah. "It's going to fall into the stream! It will be ruined before Cousin Harvest Mouse even sees it!"

"Don't fret, Sarah, I'll get it!" cried Ernest, jumping up, ready to leap into the stream.

But before Ernest could jump into the water, a figure appeared among the ripples, and seized the hat just before it touched the water.

"Your hat, Mistress Mouse, ma'am," said a gruff voice.

And onto the bank stepped a stranger, his clothes damp and bedraggled and his reddish fur and long, flattened tail dripping wet.

THE WOOD MOUSE

Mice like Sarah live in the fields and hedgerows, running and jumping into the bushes in search of fruit and berries. Sometimes they live in an old bird's nest or a grass nest shaped like a globe which they hide under a pile of dead leaves.

94

THE HARVEST MOUSE

The harvest mouse is very small. It lives in the cornfields, climbing up the stalks to pick ears of corn to eat. When winter comes the harvest mouse seeks a new home in the farmer's barn or in a haystack.

"Thank you kindly," cried Sarah, seizing her precious hat with both paws. "But you are surely a stranger here. Won't you please tell us your name?"

"I'm Ben Beaver, ma'am," replied the stranger, with a little bow.

97

Beavers are large water-dwelling rodents. They love to eat and gnaw tree bark. When they are alarmed, they slap the water with their tails to warn others that danger is near. A beaver's home is called a **lodge**.

"Where have you come from?" asked Martin eagerly.
"I'm a pedlar by trade," replied Ben, "and I travel the countryside with my family, selling my wares. They have just gone upstream to explore. We all think this is the prettiest place we have ever seen."
Everyone looked very pleased at this, and they all smiled in a most friendly fashion at Ben.

98

"What kind of things do you sell?" asked Hubert, curiously.

"Wooden goods of all kinds," replied Ben. "Walking sticks, carved plates, umbrella handles, and even musical instruments. My pack is over there by the willow tree. Please take a look inside if you wish!"

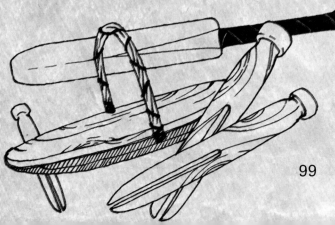

Baskets, cricket bats, garden trugs and clothes pegs are all made from different types of willow trees.

99

Everyone crowded around Ben as he untied his pack. The shrews and the rabbit twins, who had been playing hide and seek upstream, came to see what all the excitement was about.

"Oh, Ben, I like this!" cried Hubert, picking up a stout walking stick with a comfortable paw-rest at the top. "Just the thing for a long country walk. I'll take it, please."

"What pretty plates!" cried Sarah to Marmaduke, pointing to a set of six, each with a design of holly berries on it. "They will look so elegant on the table tomorrow when Granny Hermione comes to tea."

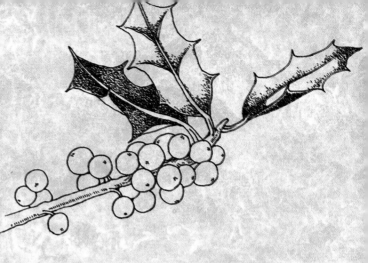

The holly is an evergreen shrub with dark glossy leaves and deep scarlet berries. We decorate homes with holly at Christmas, and the robins search eagerly for the berries to eat in winter when food is scarce.

"Especially if they are filled with Granny's seed cake and codlins and cream buns," chuckled Cedric cheekily. The little shrew looked longingly at the wooden flutes, as did his Countrylane friends.

"Here, children, take a flute each!" cried Ben generously. "And I'll make you a cricket bat and some peg dolls when I find time."

Marmaduke, who loved music more than anyone else in Countrylane, could scarcely believe his eyes when he saw the beautifully carved violin. "Did you make that?" he gasped. "You must be a true craftsman."

Ben blushed with pleasure and the skin around his nose turned bright pink. "It took me a long time," he admitted. "I used only the best spruce and sycamore wood."

"If you let me buy it, I will treasure it always!" promised Marmaduke.

Smiling, Ben handed it over.

Just then Hermione Hamster came bustling up. "Come and dry your clothes at my house," she cried briskly. "Mrs Beaver and young Bill are there already . . . and we've thought of a good idea. Why don't you stay here in Countrylane instead of travelling about? We can find you lots to do."

"Yes, you can make me a new number plate for my car," cried Harold Hedgehog, driving up at that moment.

"You can make and sell birch brooms, carved bowls and ornaments, storage jars for rowan and bramble jelly . . .oh, there are lots of jobs," added Hubert, who liked the look of Ben Beaver very much. "Professor Torquillian needs lots of bowls for his experiments, and Mrs. Badger never has enough clothes pegs! And you could be our official Countrylane Rescuer."

Ben looked rather puzzled until Harold Hedgehog explained. "We would call on you if anyone was trapped in a tree or locked out of a house."

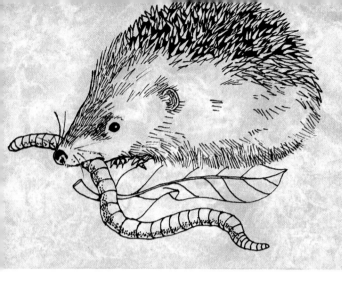

Hedgehogs go to sleep in winter, usually in a hole in a hedgerow, and doze until the warmer days come again. When they are attacked, hedgehogs roll up into a prickly ball . . .no one can eat a mouthful of prickles!

And Ben was quite delighted with Hermione's plan. He went off to dry out his clothes, and then he set to work to build himself a house for his family.
All his new friends came along to watch Ben at work.

ANIMAL HOMES

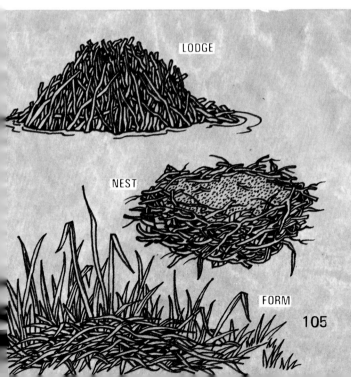

LODGE

NEST

FORM

Many animal homes have different names. A beaver lives in a *lodge*, a squirrel lives in a *drey*, hamsters and rabbits live in a *warren*, a hare lives in a *form*, a badger lives in a *set*, a shrew lives in a *nest* and a stoat also makes a *nest!*

105

First of all Ben built a dam to raise the water level of the stream. The dam was made of logs and twigs, and the cracks soon filled up with mud brought down by the stream. The pool behind the dam was the site for Ben's dome shaped lodge. The lodge only had one large room, but it was quite big enough for Ben's family.

"Now I know what busy as a beaver means," whispered Cedric Shrew to Hubert. "Doesn't he work hard? And he really is a kind beaver. He even gave Edgar a carved love spoon when he heard he was courting Selina."

"Yes, he's a real asset to Countrylane," agreed Hubert. "I do hope he will stay, and not get wanderlust feet like old Ramsbottom Rat. *He's* here one day and gone the next!"

The Brown Rat lives in the country and is no friend of the farmer! It steals from the chicken runs, swims after the ducklings and searches for the mangolds which the farmer stores away from the frost. He is a very naughty rat!

107

But old Hubert Hamster need not have worried. At the end of his busy day Ben took a long, happy look at his new home.
Outside the door was a beautifully carved sign which said:

HOME SWEET HOME
BEN BEAVER
BEAVER LODGE
MASTER CARVER AND JOINER
OFFICIAL COUNTRYLANE RESCUER
ALWAYS ON CALL

Ben sighed contentedly. Mrs Beaver was busy in her kitchen corner making supper, young Bill was fast asleep in bed, and Ben had found himself a new home and a new job. He would never leave Countrylane again.

FOOD STORE

Ben is a wise old beaver and so he stores up piles of food beneath the water during the summer months, so that his family will have plenty to eat in the cold winter days when food is scarce.

HOME SWEET HOME

Barry